COLOURING BOOK

The Alligator logo is a registered trademark of Alligator Products Ltd.

Published in 2021 by Alligator Products Ltd
2nd Floor, 314 Regents Park Road
London N3 2JX.

Printed in China.3319

www.alligatorbooks.co.uk

© 2021 Moonbug™ Entertainment. All Rights Reserved.

This is the letter A

Trace the letter A and a.
Then colour in the apple and the ant.

© 2021 Moonbug™ Entertainment. All Rights Reserved.

A is for animals.

Draw another animal on the farm in the space below. Then colour in the picture.

© 2021 Moonbug™ Entertainment. All Rights Reserved.

This is the letter B

Trace the letter B and b.
Then colour in the banana and the bear.

© 2021 Moonbug™ Entertainment. All Rights Reserved.

This is the letter C

Trace the letter C and c.
Then colour in the car and the cat.

© 2021 Moonbug™ Entertainment. All Rights Reserved.

This is the letter D

Trace the letter D and d.
Then colour in the donut and the duck.

© 2021 Moonbug™ Entertainment. All Rights Reserved.

Design a dress for Yoyo

Dress begins with a D.
Design Yoyo's dress and colour it in.

© 2021 Moonbug™ Entertainment. All Rights Reserved.

This is the letter E

Trace the letter E and e.
Then colour in the egg and the elephant.

© 2021 Moonbug™ Entertainment. All Rights Reserved.

This is the letter F

Trace the letter F and f.
Then colour in the fish and the frog.

CoComelon

FISH

FROG

© 2021 Moonbug™ Entertainment. All Rights Reserved.

This is the letter G

Trace the letter G and g.
Then colour in the grapes and the giraffe.

GRAPE | GIRAFFE

© 2021 Moonbug™ Entertainment. All Rights Reserved.

This is the letter H

Trace the letter H and h.
Then colour in the house and the hippo.

© 2021 Moonbug™ Entertainment. All Rights Reserved.

This is the letter I

Trace the letter I and i.
Then colour in the ice cream and the iguana.

ICE CREAM | IGUANA

© 2021 Moonbug™ Entertainment. All Rights Reserved.

This is the letter J

Trace the letter J and j.
Then colour in the jaguar and the jellybeans.

Cocomelon

J   j

JAGUAR   JELLYBEAN

© 2021 Moonbug™ Entertainment. All Rights Reserved.

This is the letter K

Trace the letter K and k.
Then colour in the kite and the kangaroo.

KITE   KANGAROO

© 2021 Moonbug™ Entertainment. All Rights Reserved.

This is the letter L

Trace the letter L and l.
Then colour in the lemon and the lion.

LEMON

LION

© 2021 Moonbug™ Entertainment. All Rights Reserved.

This is the letter M

Trace the letter M and m.
Then colour in the mushroom and the mouse.

MUSHROOM | MOUSE

© 2021 Moonbug™ Entertainment. All Rights Reserved.

This is the letter N

Trace the letter N and n.
Then colour in the nest and the newt.

© 2021 Moonbug™ Entertainment. All Rights Reserved.

This is the letter O

Trace the letter O and o.
Then colour in the orange and the owl.

ORANGE

OWL

© 2021 Moonbug™ Entertainment. All Rights Reserved.

This is the letter P

Trace the letter P and p.
Then colour in the pumpkin and the pig.

PUMPKIN

PIG

© 2021 Moonbug™ Entertainment. All Rights Reserved.

This is the letter Q

Trace the letter Q and q.
Then colour in the quilt and the queen.

QUILT QUEEN

© 2021 Moonbug™ Entertainment. All Rights Reserved.

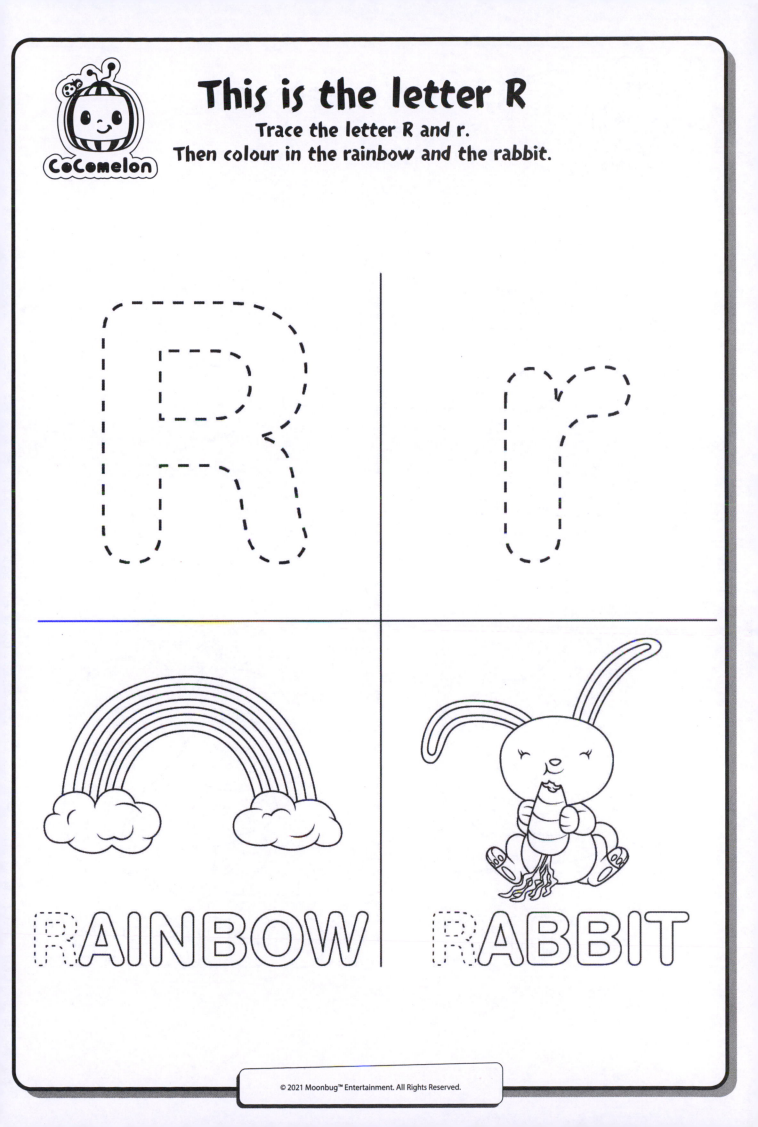

This is the letter R

Trace the letter R and r.
Then colour in the rainbow and the rabbit.

© 2021 Moonbug™ Entertainment. All Rights Reserved.

This is the letter S

Trace the letter S and s.
Then colour in the sun and the squirrel.

SUN   SQUIRREL

© 2021 Moonbug™ Entertainment. All Rights Reserved.

Count the Sheep

Sheep begins with an S.
Can you count how many sheep there are?
Then colour in the picture.

© 2021 Moonbug™ Entertainment. All Rights Reserved.

CoComelon

This is the letter T

Trace the letter T and t.
Then colour in the train and the turtle.

TRAIN

TURTLE

© 2021 Moonbug™ Entertainment. All Rights Reserved.

Tom Tom with T

Colour in this picture of Tom Tom.

© 2021 Moonbug™ Entertainment. All Rights Reserved.

This is the letter U

Trace the letter U and u.
Then colour in the umbrella and the unicorn.

© 2021 Moonbug™ Entertainment. All Rights Reserved.

This is the letter V

Trace the letter V and v.
Then colour in the violin and the vulture.

VIOLIN | VULTURE

© 2021 Moonbug™ Entertainment. All Rights Reserved.

This is the letter W

Trace the letter W and w.
Then colour in the watermelon and the wolf.

WATERMELON | WOLF

© 2021 Moonbug™ Entertainment. All Rights Reserved.

This is the letter X

Trace the letter X and x.
Then colour in the x-ray fish and the xylophone.

X-RAY FISH | XYLOPHONE

© 2021 Moonbug™ Entertainment. All Rights Reserved.

This is the letter Y

Trace the letter Y and y.
Then colour in Yoyo and the yak.

YOYO

YAK

© 2021 Moonbug™ Entertainment. All Rights Reserved.

Yo-yo begins with a Y

Yoyo is excellent with the yo-yo.
Colour in this picture of Yoyo.

© 2021 Moonbug™ Entertainment. All Rights Reserved.

This is the letter Z

Trace the letter Z and z.
Then colour in the zipper and the zebra.

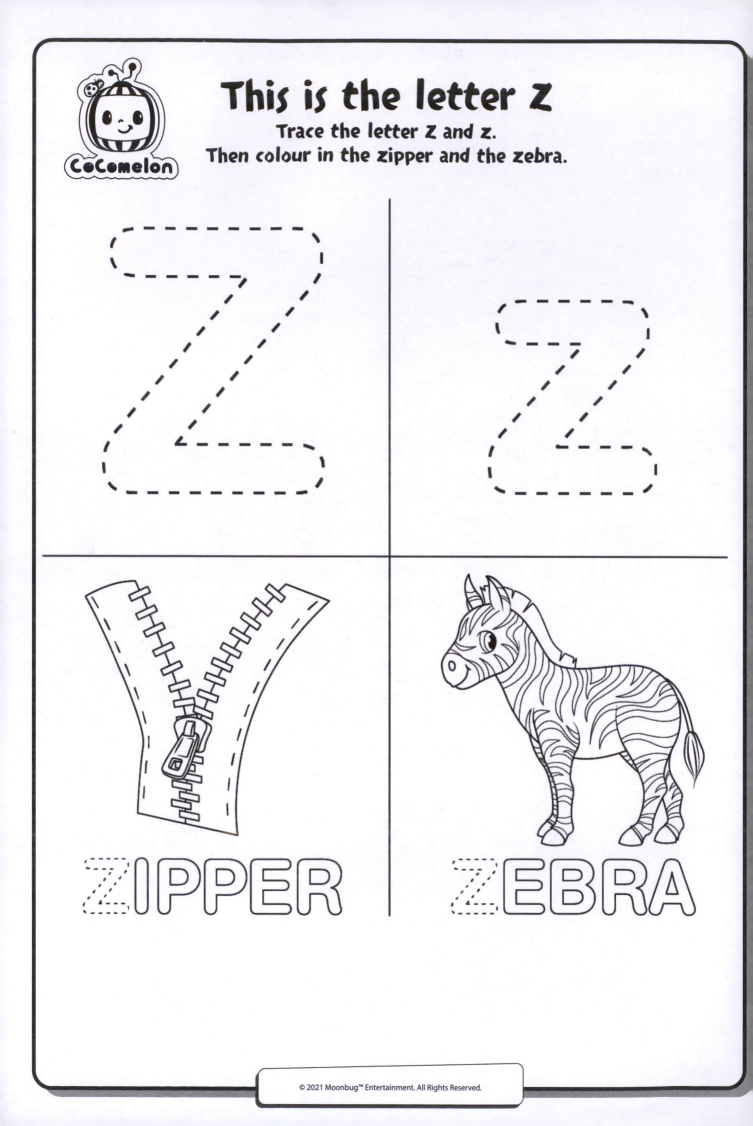

ZIPPER   ZEBRA

© 2021 Moonbug™ Entertainment. All Rights Reserved.